MW00647615

The Best of the
Mississippi   River
Ghosts

by Bruce Carlson

* * * * * * * * * *

Although the author has exhaustively researched all sources to ensure the accuracy and completeness of the information contained in this book, he assumes no responsibility for errors, inaccuracies, omissions, or any inconsistency herein. Any slights of people or organizations are unintentional. Readers should consult an attorney or accountant for specific applications to their individual publishing ventures.

Quixote
Press
1(800) 571-BOOK

DEDICATION

I want to dedicate this book to my wife, Marilyn Carlson. She has put up with countless nights of my banging away on my old Underwood typewriter while writing this book. She expected, and certainly deserved, some respite from that after previous books I have written. But, Ah, rest was not to come. She had to suffer through this one, also.

The author wants to express his appreciation to the many people who have been invaluable help by sharing family records and personal experiences. Without that help, this book would be only the front and a back cover.

TABLE OF CONTENTS

FOREWORD

All the folks who live or travel along the Mississippi River are well aware of things and places like the river itself, and Davenport. Most of them have at least heard of Fort Madison, Lake Pepin, and Galena. But, how many know about the hanging tree, the ghost of the river bend, persistent stains, or the horse that left no tracks.

Bruce Carlson's The Best of the Mississippi River Ghosts is an immensely readable collection of ghost stories from that beautiful part of our country.

There will unboubtedly be a few readers who will be able to put this book down before finishing it. However, I don't think there will be many who can do it. Readers will be hooked on this book all the way through to the end of the last chapter.

Professor Phil Hey
Briar Cliff College
Sioux City, Iowa

PREFACE

The reader will find, in this book, a collection of tales about ghosts of the Mississippi River.

The events described in this volume cover the period from the 1880s to 1985. They are, however, not in chronological or any other order. Each is a separate chapter, unrelated to any of the others.

Whenever possible, diligent effort was made to confirm these stories by getting information from other sources. That was, of course, not always possible. Ghost stories are often known to only a very small number of people.

The reader must appreciate the fact that some of these stories could cause embarrassment to people living today. Because of that, some of the stories use fictitious names. In those cases, it should be understood that any similarity to actual people, living or dead, is purely coincidental.

The author hopes that this book will serve to document some of the tales heretofore only handed down by word of mouth. They are part of the heritage of our river and deserve to be preserved.

It is emphasized that these are in the nature of folks tales. If the reader islooking for sensational stories of blood and gore, he won't find them here. If he is looking for stories with a heavy religious orientation, he had better look elsewhere. If, however, some pleasant (and hopefully, accurate) accounts of ghosts who have resided here along the river appeal to you, I invite you to spend a few hours with me in The Best of the Mississippi River Ghosts.

THE PRAIRIE SCHOONER

It was common knowledge among the farmers south of St. Paul that Niels Ingraham was a bit touched, but nobody gave it much concern. Niels wasn't one to offer anyone any trouble. He just did his nutty little things for his own enjoyment or their usefulness in helping with his work.

Niels came to the area in the 1880s and set up farming. Where he came from, and how he got here wasn't known.

He was apparently something of a genius as well as being a bit crazy. On occasion those two characteristics are difficult to distinguish one from the other. He was very handy and imaginative and developed quite a few unique gadgets. In addition to those related to farm work, he invented some games and an early version of what we call strollers today for toddlers. Why he worked on that stroller is anybody's guess. He had neither wife nor children.

At some point, Niels developed an intense interest in the praire schooners that carried families west. As the reader probably

knows, these long wagons with large white canvas covers got their name from their similarity in appearance to sail-driven schooners of the sea. The only sea these things sailed, of course, was the sea of grass in the central and western United States.

Niels was inspired by those schooners and apparently decided to build a real prairie schooner; one that would really sail on land.

So that he did. He modified a farm wagon and attached a mast to carry sails.

That sail wagon was simply another of Neils' crazy ideas so it didn't attract a whole lot of attention. He got the job done and spent a lot of windy summer afternoons sailing around on his brand new toy he built up out of pieces of this and that around the farm.

A few of the neighbors would come over to watch the "spectacle" on occasion. While Neils might have considered the "spectacle" to be his sailwagon, it was actually Niels himself that was the attraction.

Niels was reported to have absolutely no fear when it came to his sailwagon. He would run it full tilt out across the rough pasture. More than once he tipped it over, a couple of times he ended up with it in his lap.

I can just feel what the reader will be thinking at this point in the story. He/She is probably envisioning that the story will go on and tell of how Niels was

killed with his contraption, and that for years after that was seen sailing his sailwagon in that pasture south of St. Paul.

Sorry, dear reader, but you're wrong. What is actually reported to have happened is that the hogs got Niels and killed him. Then he was seen sailing his sailwagon in that pasture south of St. Paul for several years. Not quite as poetic or romantic as getting killed on the sailwagon, but that's the way the story goes.

The story tells of some sightings of that sailwagon after Niels' death, but none of these was reported to be really well-defined or seen by more than one person at the same time. Several of the times the sightings were supposed to have been by children. Perhaps they are the product of over-active imaginations or wishful thinking. Perhaps that, however, is fitting. Maybe Niels with his very active imagination would have preferred to have been imagined rather than actually seen.

Whatever the validity of the reports, they don't tell of Niels having been sighted for many, many years now, so he has apparently found his rest.

THE DANCERS

This story was told to me by a Mrs. Charles Lynn, now living out of state, but who was raised by her parents in a large old Victorian house in St. Paul. Mrs. Lynn recalls her parents' home with particular fondness. Her father, Mr. Nelson, bought that old house in the early 1920s. He and Mrs. Nelson dearly loved that house and tried, with little success, to learn the history of the place. Apparently, it had been owned by a relatively large number of people through the

years and there were some gaps in what they were able to find out. Some old papers in the house suggested that the early occupants were in some manner associated with the business of transporting or processing the logs that came down the Mississippi in huge rafts back in the old days.

The Nelsons learned that the third floor of that house had been a ballroom. The entire floor was one large room, except for a couple of small dressing rooms off to the side. In one of those dressing rooms, they found some old photos that showed some people, views of the house, and even the fancy carriages that apparently brought the guests to the home.

Mrs. Lynn told of how she would spend hours in the ballroom, studying those old photos. She told me of how she had been so impressed, as a girl, by what must have gone on in their house with all the fancy social events that were held there.

"The best part of the whole thing I missed out on, though. It was after I had gone off to college when Mother and Dad started to hear all the activity up there."

"What activity was that?" I asked.

"Well, it all started with the music. They would hear music coming from up on the third floor. They thought, at first, they were imagining it. One night, however, it was so pronounced they knew it could not be their imaginations.

They went upstairs and unlocked that ball-room door. There was no electricity up in that room, but it was a bright, moon-lit night and they could clearly see figures of men and women dancing. They were all done up in the old-fashioned clothing of thirty or forty years earlier back when the house hosted those fancy parties.

Mother and Dad spoke especially of one of the figures. It was a lady, and a particularly beautiful one. The more they talked about that lady, the more she sounded familiar to me. It started to sound like a young lady shown in one of those old photos I had looked at as a child."

"You mean they could see them that clearly?" I asked.

"Yes, Mother and Dad said they looked almost real, just slightly out of focus, but clear enough that they could easily see the peoples' features."

I asked Mrs. Lynn if her parents were afraid.

"I guess they were at first, but not as time went on. They went up there three or four times when they would hear that music. They saw the group each time, but only twice was it moon-lit enough to see them well. Each time they would do that, they would be there but a few minutes before the music would stop and the people would just kind of evaporate.

But, I was telling you about this one lady they both mentioned. After they talked about her a couple of times and I felt she sounded like one of the women in one of those old photos, I tried a little experiment with my parents.

I sorted through those old photos one week-end when I was home from college and found the one their description reminded me of. I took that one and buried it in with another dozen or so photos of women. I showed Mother and dad all those photos, being sure that the other one of them couldn't prompt them. In both cases, when we came to the one I mentioned, they told me that the woman they so much admired looked exactly like the one in the photo."

"So you believe that your parents saw a ghost of that particular woman, right?"

"I have no doubt of it. Both Mother and Dad said they definitely recognized that woman. They arrived at those conclusions without prompting from each other. Like I said, I showed those pictures to them without the other around."

"So, is the house still standing?" I asked.

"Unfortunately, no. Its been torn down for many years now. I've often wondered whatever became of those dancers and especially that beautiful young lady in her lovely gown."

It's hard to guess at where Mrs. Lynn's wishful thinking and her parents' imagination leaves off and reality begins. Maybe those dancers were there, maybe not.

BROKEN WIRES

reg Patton who lived on the banks of the Mississippi outside of Alma, Wisconsin, kept in close contact with his elderly mother quite regularly for several years. He'd call to check on her at least once a day. She, in turn, often called him "just to chat." Since their homes were only three miles apart, Greg would often go over there to do things for her.

Mrs. Patton enjoyed good health for most of her elderly years. Toward the end, she suffered from heart trouble and eventually died of it.

Her death took place in June during the early 1920s. Mrs. Patton called to talk to Greg. He couldn't help but notice that his mother sounded a bit strange that day. For one thing, she was not a demonstrative sort of person, yet that day she told Greg of how much she loved him. She said other things that Greg thought were out of character for his mother.

Greg mulled this over for a few minutes and then decided to go over to her house to see if she was okay. As he pulled out of his lane, he was surprised to find a crew at his gate working on a large tree that had fallen onto the telephone line, completely cutting the wires. There had been a storm during the night, but he had used the phone

 just a few minutes earlier so he knew that the tree had to have fallen in the past few minutes. He thought that the crew certainly had gotten there quickly. Greg spoke of that to the crew foreman.

"You guys sure do work fast."

"Why, what do you mean? We've been on this mess for almost four hours now. We got here early this morning. We ought to have this all.............."

"But, wait a minute," Greg interrupted. You couldn't have. These lines sure haven't been down for four hours. I was using my telephone not fifteen minutes ago."

The foreman looked at Greg for a minute.

"If you live up this lane here, you sure did not use your phone this morning at all. The wires are all broken. You can see that for yourself."

Greg wasn't of a mind to argue about it. He knew that he had used his phone just minutes ago, and that's all that counted. He was at a loss to figure out how he could, with those wires broken. All he knew was that he did.

The foreman watched Greg as he climbed into his car and left.

Greg soon forgot the issue as he pulled into his mother's driveway. When he entered the house, he knew that there was something wrong.

Greg found his mother in bed; dead.

The doctor established that Mrs. Patton had died of a heart attack and that she had probably died about twelve hours prior to Greg finding her.

THE RACING SCALAWAG

In cases of ghost stories there is always the point when the thing is judged, or at least claimed, to be a ghost. Such claims are made by ordinary citizens. Sometimes there is disagreement among people as to whether or not such claims are valid. Rarely, however, does anybody of government concern itself with the issue, much less deliver an opinion on the subject.

There was a situation in Wabasha, Minnesota, however, that was altogether different.

It all started over a hundred years ago. It was repeated several times in the quarter century between then and 1900.

The course of events would be pretty much the same in each case. A person would be driving along minding his own business and he would hear the approach of another buggy from behind him. This, of course, was not uncommon. Horse-drawn vehicles would travel at different speeds, depending on the vehicle or the horse. It would depend on the urgency of the driver and so forth.

The situation that existed there in Wabasha
was a rather severe problem. On occasion,
that approaching buggy from behind proved
to be an individual called "The Racing
Scalawag." He was undoubtedly a scalawag
because he would invariably cause the horse
he passed to panic and run. The "Racing"
was not quite true because no one ever
actually saw him try to race the buggy he

would be overtaking. He would just manage
to cause all kinds of havoc just by driving
by.

An interesting point about this is that he
would make no obvious attempts to annoy or
disturb the other horse. It just always
worked out that way. The horse would take
one look at the individual and just plain
go goofy. Lots of buggies, wagons, hay-
racks, etc., were destroyed and several men
sustained serious injuries as a result of
their horse running away with them.

There was lots of interest here in the
community regarding who the culprit was.
Several men were quite ready to do a number
on him if they could just find out the
identity of the man. No one ever recognized the errant driver or his horse.

After such incidents happened numerous
times, the law was called in on the case.
The sheriff's office conducted a rather

lengthy investigation as did the police, who for some reason, came down from Red Wing.

Collaring such culprits was considerably more difficult back in those days before radios. Eventually, however, the long arm of the law closed in on the man. They had him trapped in a section of road down by the Zumbrota where they knew there would be no escape, but he gave them the slip.

Another time they had him cornered when they saw him drive into a barn near Lake City. They had the barn completely surrounded, yet "The Racing Scalawag," his horse, and his buggy were not to be found in there.

It was after these two incidents that the officals of the area declared that "The Racing Scalawag" was a ghost, pure and simple. This theory made a lot of sense. It not only explained how he could get out of an escape-proof trap, but also why horses would panic when they saw him.

Apparently, the fact that he was supernatural was known to the horses in the community from the very beginning, but not to the people.

For some reason, the incidents stopped after this declaration of the nature of "The Racing Scalawag." Perhaps, if it was a ghost, the fun went out of it after he was found out. Maybe if he wasn't a ghost, he might have decided that it was a good time to hang it all up, now that someone else had gotten the blame for it.

LARS AND OTTO

My source of information for this story is a man in Hastings, Minnesota, who showed me the yellowed and faded account of the incident. He had gotten the account from his mother. She, in turn, got it from her parents.

The events recorded on those old sheets of paper were some experienced by my contact's grandfather. The old man's name was Harold Vetter and lived at the the time of the story, in Minneapolis.

Harold Vetter was a personable sort of fellow and fell into conversation with a couple of men he met on the street. One thing led to another and they ended up in a coffee shop where they could pass the time of day in a little more comfort than there on the streets of Minneapolis.

Before the trio broke up, they agreed to get together the following evening at Harold's home for a few hands of poker. That evening Harold was telling his wife about meeting the two fellows and the forthcoming poker game.

As Mrs. Vetter questioned Harold about them, it became apparent that he didn't really know much about the two, other than their names; Lars and Otto.

Mrs. Vetter had some real serious reservations about the whole affair. She thought in terms of the facts that they were strangers, poker players, and had talked with her husband for some time and managed to reveal almost nothing about themselves. With a real sense of foreboding, she could envision her grocery money for the next few weeks being pocketed by that pair. Worse yet, Harold might get carried away and lose their home to them.

Harold dismissed her concerns with a wave of his cigar and assured her that she had nothing to worry about. She wasn't too sure of that but figured there wasn't a whole lot she could do about it.

The next night brought Lars and Otto to the Vetter home and the game commenced. Each of the pair puffed away on a pipe while Harold contributed to the proper atmosphere for a poker game with his smelly old cigar.

Mrs. Vetter didn't know much about poker, but she did know enough to realize that she could not be hanging around too close

because poker players didn't appreciate a non-player very near the action. She did, however, walk by the doorway a few times during the evening to see if she could tell how well Harold was doing. She also had the foresight to serve coffee to the men for an excuse to go in there to the table a few times. The first time or two she was in the room all she saw was three guys playing poker. As the night wore on, however, some strange things began to happen.

She was checking the three of them once and noticed that the one named Otto was missing a foot. This really caught her by surprise. She hadn't noticed that missing member or that he was limping when he came in. She didn't object to her husband playing poker with a guy missing a foot, but only if he came in with one gone. She was sure the fellow had two feet when he got there.  She didn't remember him having a cane and she would certainly have seen if he had been on crutches!

As she went back into the kitchen, she thought more about the situation. She knew she had to be wrong either about the foot being gone, or about the fellow's condition when he came in. The more she thought about that situation, the more troubled she became.

Mrs. Vetter's next trip to the parlor with some things for the fellows to munch on was a good excuse for her to examine Otto a little more carefully. Maybe she just didn't see that foot in the shadows of the table. After all, an overhead lamp was the

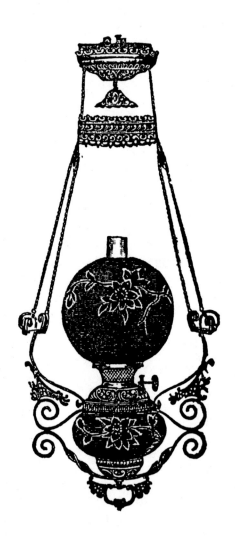

only illumination in there. She went on in with a tray of goodies and studied Otto very carefully. Sure enough, there that foot was gone all right. She decided to dismiss it all as a simple matter of not being properly observant when the two men came in that evening. She was about to turn to leave the room when she saw that Lars was missing an entire left leg.

Mrs. Vetter almost dropped the tray on the table in her shock. She knew she could have been wrong about Otto's foot, but she was absolutely sure that the other guy came in with both legs. But as she studied Lars, there was no denying it. The leg was gone. Even the pant leg was gone. Looking at the men at the table, she could see that they were playing just as if nothing was wrong. There was nothing about the upper bodies of the two to suggest that anything was wrong, but there sure was under the table.

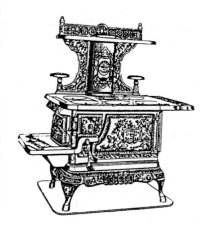

Mrs. Vetter kept her composure long enough to get back to the comfortable familiarity of her kitchen stove. She was about to call Harold to tell him what was happening. Just then, however, she heard the men talking about breaking up, one of them saying something about the hour being late and the need to arise early in the morning. Making her legs go when they would hardly support her, she groped her way back to the parlor. As she entered the doorway, her eyes sought the underside of the table again. If she could have, she would have cried out, but her throat was tight and she could hardly breathe. Both legs of both men were gone, completely and totally gone. Harold was obviously unaware of what was going on. From his perspective, everything was apparently all right.

Just then, the three of them dropped their cards on the table and got ready to rise from their chairs. It was then that Harold would join his wife in witnessing a scene that neither of them would ever forget. The rest of the bodies of Otto and Lars just faded and were gone. One pipe clattered to the floor and the other fell on the table. Suddenly, where there had been four people, now there were only two.

It was she who first regained the use of her voice. She told Harold of what she had seen those few minutes before he was aware of what was happening. The two of them discussed the event on through the night.

It was during that time that Mrs. Vetter

40

made a detailed record of exactly what happened.

It is that record that rests yet today in a safety deposit vault in a Minneapolis bank. One thing it doesn't reveal is the thing that Mrs. vetter started out worrying about so much. It doesn't tell if Harold won or lost that night. I guess after an experience like that it really doesn't make much difference.

THE CHORE GHOST

If there is one thing I've learned about ghosts in the research for this book, it's that there is just plain no predicting what they will do next. One would think, for example, that when a person joins the world of eternity, he would soon forget the worries and concerns of this work-a-day world. But, as I say, you just can't tell about those critters.

The young honey who haunted a house in Guttenburg, Iowa, for instance certainly didn't forget the everday world she left. Who she was or where she came from, no one ever did figure out. Apparently, however, she was a girl who knew how to work when she was alive, for she sure did as a ghost.

The gal must have lived in that house in Guttenburg at one time, for she certainly took care of it. The owners back in 1910, Mr. and Mrs. Hohlman, were of mixed minds about their ghost. They appreciated the willingness of the gal to work but would have preferred a more mortal one that would do what they wanted rather than what she wanted.

One day the couple had been gone for several hours. As they went up their front

walk when they returned, they could distinctly hear the sound of pounding coming from within tne house. The concerned pair hurried on in to see what was happening. They could tell the sound was coming from an upstairs bedroom. With some hesitation, they went up the stairs and opened the door to that bedroom. One can only imagine their surprise when they saw a young girl busily pounding tacks into the edge of the carpet as she was stretching it with a very real and worldly carpet stretcher.

The girl looked up as they entered the room and calmly put the hammer down, stood up, dusted herself off, and strolled through a perfectly sound wall to disappear. The Hohlmans were not a flightly or fanciful pair so were dismayed and unable to figure out what was happening. This was not, however, the first such encounter so they finally accepted it as simply another of the strange goings-on in their home.

Another time their spirtual guest scrubbed their kitchen floor for them. Disconcert-ing as that was, it was at least something that Mrs. Hohlman ap-preciated having had done for her. The couple joked about their odd helper

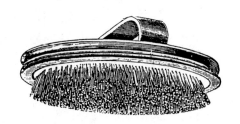

and told each other they wished that the gal would become interested in other practical things like doing the laundry or working in the garden.

Sometimes the girl's efforts caused more trouble than they were worth. The most not-able of those times was when she proceed-ed to paint the exterior of the house. The building didn't need painting and her starting that job necessitated Mr. Hohlman finishing it. Fortunately, the gal used white paint so it was easy to match it on Mr. Hohlman's part. Mr. Hohlman was asked by a neighbor why he was painting the house when it so obviously didn't need it. He

mumbled something about doing it since it would be needing it before long, anyway.

Apparently the Hohlmans didn't tell others outside the family about their problem. It was from their nephew in Dubuque that I learned of the whole situation.

What little checking I was able to do with descendants of subsequent owners and occupants of the house, it appears that no one else was bothered by the chore girl of Guttenburg.

A SHORT STAY

In 1965, a young couple in Winona by the name of Kent and Lynn Teterman moved into a modest house outside of town. They hadn't planned to stay there long. He was scheduled to be leaving for the service, and they would be moving again within a few months.

Kent and Lynn had no idea when they moved stuff into that house how really short a time they would be staying. It amounted to no more than a few hours.

This young couple was yet unencumbered

with a whole lot of the world's possesions
so they got moved in within the span of
only a couple of hours' time. They sorted
their stuff, tied up their little dog, and
went out to get a sandwich. Within an hour
or so, they returned and went to bed.

They hadn't been in bed but a few minutes
and they were jolted upright with a pierc-
ing scream that seemed to come from the
attic. They hardly had time to get a
"What's that?" out before they were hit
with a second surprise. The ceiling and
one wall of the room glowed with a cool
blue light. It wasn't bright, but there
was enough light to cast shadows in the
room. While they were trying to recover
from that, the scream came
again from the attic. At the
same time, a cold breeze
brushed its way through the
room on that windless, hot
night. There was a sudden and
pronounced drop in temperature
that persisted even after that
brief cold breeze had passed.

A couple of phone calls to
borrow a pickup truck, a
hurried session of pitching
their goods into that truck,
and the Tetermans were moved
out again, a scant few hours
after moving in.

Later Kent learned that the
house was supposed to have
been haunted. They didn't
know if what they heard and
saw constituted a haunting,
but they did know it was a
very, very spooky experience.

THE GHOST IN THE BARN

he old gent from Maiden Rock, Wisconsin who told me this story about the haunted barn near Stockholm was anxious to share it with me.

"I guess I'm about the only person left who knows about that ghost in the haunted barn," he said.

"That was so long ago, I 'spect that some who saw that critter are ghosts themselves by now."

"A haunted barn?" I interrupted.

"Yep, it sure was."

With that, the old man leaned back and told me about a situation that happened over near Stockholm when he was a boy living there. I could tell he was eager to tell me the story. I don't know if it was because he wanted to reminisce or if he wanted the story to be saved, thinking he was the last one to know of it.

This ghost haunted a large old barn that had a big cupola on top. The cupola had

49

had the normal contingent of dust, pigeons, old boards and blown-in leaves common to such structures. Also, as was customary back then, it was almost a fair-sized building in its own right. Fair sized, that is, for a building sitting atop another. It had several louvered windows and a tiny trap door leading to the loft below. That trap door was the only access to that cupola and had to be wiggled through after climbing a ladder built onto a huge walnut pole that extended from the ground all the way up to the ridge of the roof.

"This here ghost had two funny habits," the old man said.

"What were they?"

"Well, for one thing, he was always a pitchin' things out those windows. There were some of the dangest stuff he threw out of there. Once he pitched a full set of workhorse harness out that window. He was always a throwin' little things like tools and kitchen stuff like pots 'n pans out that window. There was some of the dangest stuff, like I say, that he pitched out."

"What else did he do? You said he had two funny habits."

At this point I mentally made a bet with myself. I had noticed that Midwesterners seem to feel compelled to start a lot of sentences with the word "Well". I thought that this was a question that would probably get an answer starting with that word.

"Well, he used to be always a hollerin' out one of those windows to people to tell 'em to come on up. This caught a lot of strangers by surprise, being hollered at by someone to come up into a barn cupola. When the guy would get up there and squeeze through that little trap door, he'd find no one was up there at all."

I'm surprised that people would go up in that loft and climb that ladder just because some nutty character called at them," I said.

"Well," he replied, "Back then folks had a little more grit 'n guts to 'em. Today they'd likely just stand like a dummy wonderin' if the ladder was safe."

At this point the old gent commenced to deliver an impassioned lecture on the "wimps that folks are nowadays."

I got the old fellow off that lecture and
back to the barn ghost, however.

"But, couldn't it have been someone up
there just playing a trick?" I asked.

"Nope, it sure wasn't. There was just
plain no way for anyone to get out of that
cupola except down through that trapdoor or
out on the roof. That guy up there jus'
plain disappeared. He had to be a ghost.

'Nother thing was how he could do things no
human could."

"How's that?" I asked.

"Well, I'll tell ya," he continued.

"One day there was four or five fellows
there in the hog lot. They could see someone fooling around up in the cupola. The
farmer who owned the place was jus' about
ready to go up to check it out. Suddenly,
this here chair came a flyin' out of one of
those windows. It clattered and banged its
way all the length of the roof, then fell
to the ground below. The
owner of the farm and
another guy went tearing
up into that cupola to see
what was agoin' on. They
didn't find anybody up
there or any sign that
anybody had been inside it
for a while. It was kind
of a mystery, for sure."

"Did the chair belong to
the farmer?" I asked.

"I dunno know if it did or not. They did get to talkin' about that chair, though. It was pretty well beat up by the time it hit the ground, but the fellows kind of pushed 'er back together. They got to thinkin' it was too big to go through one of those little bitty windows. So they took the thing back up there by droppin' a rope down from the cupola and haulin' it up. It was sure too big to go through that little trap door inside.

"My Aunt Ella was there that day. Her and a couple of other visiting ladies came out to the lot when they saw all the excitement a goin' on.

"Well, anyway, they got that chair back up there. Sure enough, it wouldn't go through that window. They twisted and turned the thing all over a trying to get it through that window, but it wouldn't go. They saw it come out, but it sure wouldn't go back in."

I asked the old man if he had seen the ghost when he was a kid. It was almost as if he was apologizing when he told me he hadn't. I know he wished that he had. "Nope, never did, but had a bunch of kin who saw him. I told you about Aunt Ella being there the day the critter threw the

chair out the window. Well, she saw him
that day and two other times. Now Aunt
Ella jus' plain wouldn't lie. She sure
didn't believe in lying. Far as that goes,
she didn't believe in ghosts either til she
saw that 'un."

Apparently that ghost that even Aunt Ella
believed in has left the country. At least
he hasn't been seen for many years, now.

THE GHOST IN THE MIRROR

In doing the research for this book I ran into an interesting theory a couple of different times. It was that one could see a ghost but not a mirror image of one. This story, however, says just the opposite. It tells of a ghost that was seen only in a mirror.

This ghost was that of a handsome young man who appeared to be in his early to middle twenties. While he was seen from 1932 to 1937, his appearance was that of a different time; years earlier. His clothes were of a style common to the time forty or fifty years before then.

This ghost was seen several times in a modest frame house in a corner lot in Prairie du Chien.

The occupants of that house back in the 1930s for awhile were the grandparents of a Mrs. Carr who lived, outside of Eastman.

Mrs. Carr told me about the incidents involving the ghost just as she had heard them from her grandmother.

"How do you know your grandmother wasn't pulling your leg?" I asked.

"Well, you would have had to have known Grandma to know she wasn't. She was kind of a sobersided old gal and that's something she wouldn't have done."

"Did your grandmother see the ghost herself, or just hear about it?"

"Oh, she saw it all right. She and Grandpa both saw it. Twice they saw it together. Usually, though, only one of them would see it at any given time.

Mrs. Carr went on to tell me about how one of her grandparents would be in front of a mirror and see the ghost there in the glass. At one time or other they saw him in the bathroom mirror, a large bureau mirror and in one over the mantle on the fireplace in the parlor.

She told of how they would see the ghost just as plain as day in the mirror, but when they turned to look at the area, there would be nothing. On one occasion her grandfather took the opportunity to look back and forth several times. Each time he could see the ghost in the mirror but could not see him if he looked directly at the appropriate area. There was no question about it. The ghost would be seen one way, but not the other.

"It was also on this occasion that Grandpa realized that the ghost was going to be there for quite a while. He picked up a hand mirror of Grandma's and held it so he could see an image of the image. You know how you can do that and get an endless series of images."

"So what happened when he did that?" I asked.

"Grandpa saw the ghost in that second mirror also. He still couldn't see him when he looked directly at him, though."

I observed that Mrs. Carr's grandfather apparently wasn't afraid of the ghost.

"Oh, no! Neither him nor Grandma were afraid of their ghost. Not even when Grandma was home alone, was she afraid."

Mrs. Carr then went on to tell me another interesting incident. She told me about the time that her grandfather was standing near a mirror smoking his pipe. He heard a faint cough and turned to see who was behind him. There was no one there. He glanced in the mirror and there stood his ghost. Apparently even ghosts can find pipe tobacco smoke irrating at times.

"Did your grandparents ever have any idea of who the man was?" I asked.

"No, but they used to talk about that. They were of the opinion that the ghost was that of someone who had lived in the house earlier. It was an old house, even back then, and had undoubtedly been lived in by a number of people.

After talking to Mrs. Carr I managed to run down one of the children belonging to the family that lived in that house in the middle 1940s after her grandparents did. He recalled nothing ghostly about the house other than some neighbor having talked about a ghost much earlier. That, of course, was probably the one seen by Mrs. Carr's family.

The house still stands there in Prairie du Chien, but it looks a lot different now. The current residents know nothing about a ghost that haunts the mirrors in the house.

NO TRACKS

A pparently, ghosts can even be animals. The animal ghost that was supposed to have been seen on the road between Savanna and Thomson, Illinois hasn't been sighted for a long time but reported several times between 1910 and 1916.

A ghost horse was seen on that road back in those days by several people, some of whom were of unquestioned integrity. At times it was fully outfitted with a bridle and saddle. Sometimes it was without any gear on it at all.

Various people have attempted to catch the critter; some on horseback and some in cars. One young man, while driving, saw the horse. He was fortunate in that the road had just been bladed and was smooth enough to get up to over 50 miles an hour. The driver could understand how his quarry could keep out ahead of him for a short distance but was shocked when he realized that he had gone over three miles at that speed.

One morning a local farmer sighted the
horse. It was after a summer shower so he
decided to track it rather than to try to
run it down.

He was apparently the first to notice that
the critter simply didn't leave any tracks.
He expected that he could follow the horse
easily after that rain, but he was wrong.
There wasn't a track to be seen.

The horses hooves seemed to touch the dirt.
The farmer could even hear that very typical sound of a golloping horse. Neverless,
he couldn't find a mark.

A couple of the reports of this ghost horse
indicated that it had a rider, but most of
the versions had the horse quite riderless.

There have been no convincing theories as
to why that four-footed spook came to haunt
that particular road.

THE HANGING

ary Gilchrist lived in Illinois City, Illinois in the 1920's and 1930's. He had lived there earlier with his parents for a short time when he was a child in 1903. Back at that earlier time, he had heard a story about an event that was supposed to have taken place in a grove of trees along the creek south of town.

The story told of how a group of men had hung a cattle rustler from a large old tree. It told of how the hanging was lynch action and that the perpetrators had gotten all drunked up, making a grisly party out of the occasion. One of the group had supposedly hung a cow bell around the victim's neck with a loop of barbwire as a taunting gesture. That bell was said to have rung for quite a while as the man jerked and jumped there on the end of the hanging rope. Later a couple of the men had gotten rid of their own cowbells after they had sobered up and thought of their role in that sordid affair.

By the time Gary had moved back to Illinios City as an adult in the early 1920's, he had forgotten the story he heard as a child about the hanging. He moved onto a small acreage where that large old oak still grew along the creek. By then, however, much of the tree was dead.

One night during a thunderstorm that tree was hit by a bolt of lightning that destroyed most of the remaining part. Gary decided to pile the branches up and set them afire. Even as he worked on that old tree, he still didn't recall that "hanging story", much less remember that this was the tree. This was the very tree from which the man was supposed to have been hung!

Gary got the tree burning good. It was a pleasant summer evening so he tarried there stoking the fire, raking debris in, etc. Gary was sort of leaning on a rake, idly studying the fire.

All of a sudden he was struck at how a flame coming out of a knot hole was of a pattern remarkably like that of a human face. The flame curled around to form the eyes. Other wisps of fire formed the mouth, nose, and neck. Gary expected that pattern to be only momentarily evident, but it persisted even after several seconds. He was shocked at what he saw and how that pattern stayed rather than change as flames are apt to do.

Just then Mrs. Gilcrist touched his arm. She had brought him a glass of lemonade.

"Eunice, quick! Look at that flame from that knot hole. What does that look like to you?"

"My Gosh! It looks just like a person's face, just almost exactly!"

"Yeah, and it's been that way for almost a minute! Look at that! It's a perfect likeness now, all except for one ear that isn't there."

By now Mrs. Gilchrist was backing away from that sight. It was so real that she knew it was far from normal. Gary, however, edged a bit closer. Over two minutes had passed by now. The image was even clearer.

Gary recalled later that it was so real he could even discern expressions on the face. They were looks of distress and agony. The expressions would change, but the overall image remained.

"Eunice, come back! Look at that! You can even see the eyelashes! You've got to see this! Hurry!"

Suddenly the branch shifted as one will do as a pile of wood burns. Amid a shower of sparks the section with the knot hole fell down behind another. The image was gone.

Out of that shifting fire fell a cup-shaped piece of metal, dropping into the hot coals below. Gary reached for it with his rake and pulled it out onto the grass. There at his feet lay a blackened and bent cowbell strung on a loop of rusty old barb wire.

With a rush, his childhood memory of a story about a lynching came to Gary Gilchrist. He recalled the part about a cow bell having been hung around the man's neck with a piece of barbed wire. For a long time, Gary studied that bell, turning it over and over there in the grass.

The next day he asked around town about an old story regarding a hanging. He talked to several people who hadn't heard the story until he was directed to a blacksmith in Taylor Ridge "who might have heard about that."

Gary went to see the 'smith and asked him if he knew anything about a hanging years earlier near Illinois City.

"Oh, yeah, I do remember something about that. I think it had something to do with a horsethief or cattle rustler. Yeah, that's right. There was a rustler hung over there. He was a one-eared man."

NELLIE

The Tallen girls weren't any different than any others in the community north of Clinton where they lived with their parents around the turn of the century. Their home out there in the hills was a bit fancier than most, but they were normal children in every way. The two of them played most of the time with each other since there were no other children in the neighborhood except little Teddy, a neighbor boy.

The only chores the girls had was tending a

small flock of chickens so that summer of 1898 was devoted mainly to play and the children had a good time playing together.

The girls were alone much of the time. Mr. Tallen had a business in Clinton, and Mrs. Tallen spent a lot of time away from home in church and charitable work.

Mrs. Tallen was usually home for at least half a day but, on occasion, would be gone for the entire day. At those times, she would prepare a lunch for the girls and they would make it through the day rather well. A neighbor lady was in the practice of checking on the girls when their mother would be gone for very long.

This story tells of events that took place through the course of the summer, but it really came to a head on one of those days that Mrs. Wente was scheduled to check on the children.

Like most children, the Tallen girls had what their parents thought was an imaginary friend. They would tell what the three of them would do during the day and enjoyed talking about "Nellie". When little Teddy joined them there were four, of course.

The Tallens were wise enough to let the children indulge in their fantasy, knowing that such a thing was common among children and would be of no harm. At least, they thought they were sensible about it.

It was on an August day when Mrs. Tallen announced that on the coming Thursday, she would be in Clinton all day long and she would have a nice lunch made for the girls. At that particular time, the girls were having a run of socializing with Teddy so they asked if he could eat with them. Their mother agreed and allowed as to how she would have to fix an extra sandwich for him.

Wednesday evening the girls announced that they would like to have Nellie eat with them, also, and that their mother wouldn't have to fix an extra sandwich for Nellie, or any at all, because Nellie had offered to fix the lunch for all four of them.

Mrs. Tallen smiled and she said that would be just fine, and she would fix them some snacks ".......just in case Nellie didn't come."

"Oh, but she'll be here and she is going to make our lunch. She is really good at that, you know."

"OK, girls, but I'll have some sandwiches ready anyway."

Little more was said about Thursday's plans except Mrs. Tallen told her husband that Nellie was coming also and the children were going to make a party of it. She told him that the girls even thought that Nellie was going to fix the lunch. He wondered out loud if the "Nellie" thing might be getting out of hand. The issue was, however, eventually dismissed and that was that.

Come Thursday, off to work went Mr. Tallen, and Mrs. Tallen went her way.

At noontime, the girls, Teddy, and Nellie all came to the house to eat. Mrs. Tallen would have been surprised to see that Nellie was real. She would have also been shocked to see that Nellie pitched right in and did, indeed, fix the meal.

Nellie was a bit young to be doing that, but she did a good job of it.

As planned, Mrs. Wente, the neighbor, came over to check on the girls. When she walked in, the four children were seated at the kitchen table, eating quite nicely.

"Oh, Mrs. Wente, we're having a real nice meal and Nellie fixed it all by herself."

"Hello, Nellie. I don't think I've seen you before. Where do you live?"

That was the first and last thing that Mrs. Wente ever said to Nellie. The little girl simply disappeared from sight. The spoon she was holding dropped from mid-air, clattering onto the table.

No amount of questioning by Mr. and Mrs. Tallen could extract from the children any meaningful information about "Nellie." She was a girl that simply showed up on occasion and was a good playmate.

Never again did Nellie come to play with the Tallen girls. There were several theories advanced as to who Nellie was, but none of them was any more convincing than another.

THE WEDDING PHOTO

The courtship of Matt Vinning and Roberta Bradford, whom he eventually married, was one marked with a lot of tension.

Matt's main competitor for Roberta's hand was a man by the name of James Shaw. James was a serious contender for the beautiful Roberta so the competition was keen.

Matt was raised on a farm near Muscatine while James was a city slicker from Davenport. This story tells of the contest between solid and unexciting Matt and the more flamboyant and urbane James Shaw. It tells of the bizarre incident that ended that contest.

During the course of the courtship of Roberta, Matt never could quite figure out why he was in the race in the first place. He considered himself to be the natural underdog in the whole affair. While he had a humdrum job on the railroad, James led the glamorous life of a photographer traveling around the countryside taking pictures of pretty ladies and well-known people. Matt knew that his attempts to impress Roberta with tales of his experiences on the railroad paled in comparison with that city slicker must have been telling her about his travels to far-away places like Iowa City, Galesburg, Peoria, and even as far away as Des Moines. It wouldn't have been too bad if Matt could recite the names of the cities he went to on the train. He couldn't even do that. His job was oiling the engines there in Muscatine, so such a recitation was out. It's kind of tough to romanticize oiling a railroad engine.

 James could tell of his experiences when visiting Des Moines. Matt could tell only of helping his father operate a still back on the farm. James' father had been a sailor on the high seas. Matt's knew only milking cows and making cheese. All in all, the cards were stacked against poor Matt. Anything he was or could do, James could out-be him or out-do him.

The ironic part of it all was that Roberta preferred Matt from the very beginning and eventually proved that by marrying him rather than James, the city slicker. This, too, came as a shock to Matt. He had been so impressed by the qualifications of his adversary that he thought Roberta should have been also. Roberta cared not a fig, however, that James' father had sailed the high seas. She had no intention of marrying the father of either one of those fellows.

Matt had been so concerned about the more glamourous James that he had tended to overlook his own good qualities. Eventually, Matt, much to his surprise, prevailed. The romance that took place in the 1890's led to their marriage  in 1901. Matt left his job on the railroad to take over his father's farm near Muscatine, and life was good to the couple. Their busy life on the farm led them to think little of James Shaw or Matt's old job on the railroad.

James continued to live in Davenport and remained single. On occasion, his path would cross that of the Vinnings'. It was very apparent that some of these encounters were arranged by James as he continued to be interested in Roberta. She had no interest in him, however. Even Matt grew confident in his relationship with his wife. All three of these people knew that James was still interested in Roberta, but he was the only one who was really concerned about it at all.

As the years wore on, one would think that James would have given it up. On the contrary, his advances became more insistent and his "chance" meetings with Roberta on the streets of Davenport even more obviously contrived.

This situation began to wear a bit thin on both Matt and Roberta. One day when James "just happened" to meet them in town, Roberta spoke up and simply told James that he would never come between Matt and her.

It wasn't long before she had occasion to recall those exact words. It was about a year after that conversation when James was killed in a fire. The newspapers reported that he suffered and died from severe smoke inhalation. Since James was an acquaintance of the Vinnings, even if not a friend, they talked about his death a bit. This led them to some reminiscences about their courtship days. Matt even confessed to

having been concerned about the fact that his father had been only a farmer and maker of whiskey while James's had been a sailor on the high seas.

The couple soon forgot James Shaw, however, and life on the farm continued.

It happened in 1908. The Vinnings had been married for almost eight years and things were going rather well for them. They had a nice home on the farm and were getting along just fine. Like all the neighbors, they had a parlor just off the front hall of the house. The parlor was only for entertaining guests so they spent little time in that room.

Among the pictures and other decorations on the parlor walls was an enlarged copy of their wedding picture. It was the classic pose in which Roberta was standing behing and to one side of Matt who was seated on and ornate chair.

After several years of marriage, the Vinnings had only infrequent occasion to look at that picture even during the few times they were in the parlor.

One day in December of 1908, Roberta was in that room cleaning up. Matt was finishing his dinner when she called for him to come to the parlor. The extremely agitated sound of her voice led him to go to her as much as did her words. When he got to the door of the parlor, he saw his wife leaning heavily on a chair back as if she was on the verge of falling. He ran to her and asked what was wrong.

Roberta could only mouth the words she tried to speak. Her throat was drawn tight, and her face and arms were white and clammy. Matt was concerned and repeatedly asked her what the problem was. Roberta finally gasped;

"......look, look at the picture!"

Matt's eyes followed hers. What he saw turned his face and neck a deep red, and then he, too, paled as he struggled to comprehend. There was that wedding picture both had seen so many times. Matt was seated on that chair. She smiled at the camera from where she had always stood. Matt, sat there rigidly on his chair as he always had. Between the couple, however stood the unmistakable figure of James Shaw!

By now, it was Roberta who was able to talk.

"How can that be?"

Matt not only didn't know, but he wouldn't have been able to tell if he did. He was totally at a loss to understand it or to even respond.

Finally the couple recovered from the shock. They sat there for almost an hour discussing the situation. Both swore that they had done nothing to that picture.

Matt went for the necessary tools and they removed the photo from behind the glass. They examined it closely. There was absolutely no evidence that the photo had been tampered with. There was no pasted-in portion. The paper was unaltered other than to show the image of James Shaw, right between Roberta and Matt. They made a second startling discovery while they were examining that photo. There came from the portion showing James, the distinct odor of burnt cloth. They thought then of how James had died of smoke inhalation.

Thus, James proved Roberta's prediction to be wrong. He finally did come between them.

Fortunately, we can report that the situation protrayed in the wedding photo failed to carry over into their lives. Roberta and Matt agreed to destroy the photo. They did that and it was the last ever seen or heard of James Shaw, the city slicker who, in a small way, came between Roberta and Matt Vinning.

THE BARREN GRAVE

I don't know if this is a ghost story or not. I really don't think it is. It's a strange tale about a grave, so that's close enough.

The grave is that of a middle-aged man. There was apparently nothing in the man's life or his death that would suggest that his grave would be anything special. The two sources of this story differ in both the man's name and the location. One version had the man a Johnston near Oak-ville, Iowa and the other had the site near Grandview, Iowa and the name being Voores. All the other details of the two stories, however, were almost identi-cal.

Whatever his name and wherever his grave, it's an interesting situation. The grave was not in a ceme-

tery. It was on the farm of the man's re-
lative on a pleasant hillside. It over-
looked the rest of the property.

The burial was preformed by the family with
the assistance of their minister. All
apparently went quite well. The grave was
right close to a nice cherry tree.

Within a couple of days after the burial,
however, the family noticed the leaves on
the tree were dying. Within a week the
tree was stone dead, and the leaves were
completely dry and brown.

This was something of a disappointment to
the family as that tree had added a lot to
the beauty of the gravesite. They decided,
however, to remove the tree rather than to
move the coffin to another place. The tree
was cut down and another planted in its
place. It was reasoned that they probably
killed the first one by cutting too many
roots, but that a new one would grow well

there.

Unfortunately, the second one died also.

This was exasperating but a third one was planted there and well-watered. It also died.

About this time, a good month had passed and it was noticed that the grass seed planted on the loose dirt hadn't started to grow.   It should have gotten a good start within a month.   It was in the early summer, but it had been moist enough for that grass to have gotten going well, but there wasn't a sign of new grass.

The family bagan to think that something out of the ordinary was going on. They replanted the tree. This time it was a cottonwood because those things can grow anyplace. They watered it well and re-seeded the dirt with more grass seed. Again, nothing. The tree died and the seed wouldn't sprout. In addition, at this time some wild flowers growing nearby died.

Those wild flowers dying really caused a lot of talk in the family. those native flowers were normally tough little things.   Something quite odd had to be going on to cause them to die! Fur-thur, a well-watered cottonwood just plain had no reason not to thrive there.

One of the men grew weary of all the talk going on within the family by now. He said,

"Let me plant a tree, and I'll fix that grass."

This man planted yet another tree and instead of seeding the site down, he brought in some good bluegrass sod, watering it well every other day.

The tree died as did the sod.

By this time, the family recognized that they had a full-fledged supernatural situation of their hands. Their answer was to pour a slab of cement over the grave site.

To this day, nothing grows on that gravesite. The cement slab appears to be the reason. Just what is going on under that slab? Why wouldn't things live, even when given extra good care?

No one knows.

THE BOX

Paul Bell lived in a little shack down by the river, not too far from Galena, Illinois.

When Paul went to check his throw lines he had set out back in 1908, he had no idea what he was getting into. It just plain wasn't going to be his day.

Paul's son Wilbur told me that his father had said:

"If I'da known what all was goin' to happen that day, I'da stood in bed."

Things actually went pretty much normal as Paul checked his lines until he got to one of the last ones. He had fallen heir to some window sash weights and he was using them as ballast to hold the end of the line out into the water. They were handy for that purpose. In fact, throw line fishermen still use those sash weights yet today. A real advantage of those as ballasts for throw lines was that they didn't tend to snag up on stuff like other things guys have used.

When Paul went to pull in that particular line, however, it was snagged on something. Even with that sash weight for a ballast, that line was still hung up down there in the water.

"Pa didn't appreciate that particular line bein' snagged up. It was new line and had new hooks on it. He figured he'd have to wade out to free it up. Sure as a guy tries to jerk a line loose, it'll break out near the ballast rather than free itself. It's the natural cussedness of things, you know."

Wilber continued on with his Pa's story about those throw lines. At this point I started to wonder if this was a ghost story or a fish'n story.

Paul waded out to free up the line and found what the problem was. It was snagged up on a large wooden box. Paul got the box half way up out of the water and saw that it was not a thrown-together hunk of junk. It was a well-made box, bolted, and with iron protectors on the edges and corners.

It certainly seemed to be worth a little
more investigation. So he wrestled that
heavy box to shore and shoved it up on the
bank, then got a tire iron to pry it open.

Paul worked on the
box with the tire
iron, anxious to
get inside of it.
He had already
noticed a strange
thing about that
box. It was very
obviously empty.
He knew there was
no way he could
have shoved it up
on the bank were
it full of water.
Yet, why wasn't it
floating, rather
than setting on
the bottom of the
Mississippi?

When he got that
lid pried open he
found that it was,
indeed, empty; ex-
cept for a lone
wad of what look-
ed to be human
hair and a few
hunks of some non-
descript rocklike
material.   That
was kind of a sur-
prise. The real
mystery, however,
was   something

else. What really surprised him was what was not in the box. There was absolutely no water in there at all. That, of course, would make sense with a glass bottle with a cork or cap, but a wooden box will invariably leak. It was a well-made box, but certainly didn't look to be tight enough to be totally waterproof. Yet there was not a drop of water in it.

It wasn't 'til an hour or so later when Paul was sitting by that box having his lunch that he suddenly realized that that box was a coffin of some sort. Those rock-like hunks were obviously bones. As he studied them, he decided that they were human bones. It was while he was looking around among those bones that he found a gold ring encircling one of them.

This new development with the ring caused Paul to be considerably less interested in the box itself. After all, what could you do with a box that was really a coffin? A nice gold ring was another matter, of course. He slid that ring onto his own finger and decided it looked just fine there.

That first night started it all. As Paul was lying in bed, he suddenly felt a severe itching on his finger that held his new windfall. He got no sleep at all, and by morning he had a red and very raw sore on that finger.

This was bad enough, but what he found in his tool shed after he got up was even worse. He had set that box on his work-bench, and every tool within two feet of it was rusted to the point of being totally useless. Then to add insult to injury, he discovered the floor of his wagon where he had placed the box was completely rotted out. The rest of the floor was in good shape, but that portion was all but gone.

"It didn't take Pa long to figure out that he had some sort of a spook problem. He could understand the possibility of a bad allergy on his finger, but those tools rusting so bad overnight and that wood floor rotting out in a few hours was something else."

"What did he do?" I asked.

"Why, Pa just pitched that ring back in the box, hauled the whole mess back to the river and dumped 'er in. He said that he sure didn't need to be plagued by a box that could pull all those tricks."

So somewhere in the Mississippi River, at or below Galena, is a wooden coffin containing a hunk of hair, some bones and a real nice gold ring.

UNREQUITED LOVE

f all the ailments to which man falls heir, one of the worst is unrequited love. To love someone and to find it unreturned can blind a person's eyes, cripple his reason, and befuddle his mind. This was no less true in 1905 than any other time.

So it was with Herbie Tinnerman who lived in the hills south of Louisiana, Missouri, back then. Herbie raised a few hogs and a little corn there on his small place. His

primary means of making a living was fishing, however. He fished the waters of the Ol' Mississippi which provided a pretty good living. His needs were modest and fishing fairly lucrative back in those days, so Herbie was doing alright.

That is, Herbie was doing alright until he suddenly realized that a neighbor girl, Louise Harding, was grown up. While Herbie was busy tending his hogs and fishing, that scrawny Harding girl up the road just seemed to grow up overnight. When Herbie was twenty-one and she but fifteen, the possibility of any romantic involvement never even occured to him. However, when he was twenty-three and she a beautiful seventeen, it was a totally different situation.

Herbie Tinnerman fell totally and incurably in love with Louise. Now, of course, being in love is a bit different than tending lines or taking care of hogs. It took entirely different approaches. Unfortunately, Herb apparently didn't appreciate that. Like most river people, Herbie wasn't one to skirt around the issue. He loved that gal so bad he was about to burst and just flat out told her; and with all the grace and finesse of a bull moose.

Louise, on the other hand, cared not a fig for big, blustery Herbie Tinnerman. She had her eyes set on going to Saint Louis and living a life of glamour and excite-

ment. Her big plans sure didn't include
a smelly old fisherman from right there in
her own unglamourous neighborhood.

Thus, Herbie had gotten himself into a real
fix. He loved Louise so much he was in im-
minent danger of exploding and she could
have cared less. He went to all kinds of
extremes to win her. He changed his
schedule so that he could drive his pony
cart past her home more often. There was
always the chance he could catch a glimpse
of her outside. He took to going to that
little church between Louisiana and
Clarksville that Louise and her family
attended.

Why, it got so bad that Herbie even con-
verted one of the hog watering barrels to a
bathtub.

All this bother got for Herbie was the
ability to recognize a couple of hymns, awfully tired out from the extra driving, and
a bit cleaner than he used to be. It also
got him a lot of "No's."

"No, you can't come to see me."

"No, you can't take me to the community picnic."

"No, I won't go to the church social with you."

"No, I won't marry you."

There were some in the community who were convinced that when Herbie's body washed a-shore down by Clarksville, that he had somehow drowned himself deliberately. Others felt that it must have been an accident. A lot of things can go wrong out  there on the Ol' Mississippi, especially when the wind whips those waves up. It never was de-termined what had happened. Herbie was gone; perhaps due to his one-way love affair, perhaps not.

For the next six years, Louise had some strange experiences. They started right after Herbie died and lasted up until the event of her marriage to Marshall Thayer from over in New Canton, Illinois.

The first of these was just a few days after the tragedy. Louise was sitting at the supper table with her family. She was asked if she'd like some of whatever dish it was that her mother was passing to her.

"I'd love some," Louise said. No sooner was that out of her mouth when she heard the very familiar and distinct voice of Herbie Tinnerman. She heard but one word.

"Yes?"

Louise looked at the others at the table, shocked to have heard that voice. No one else, however, showed any sign of having heard anything out of the ordinary.

Louise didn't say anything to anyone that day about what had happened. Nor did she a few days later when she made an observation about her plans for the day.

"I'd sure love to get to town today or tomorrow for some trading I need to do."

No sooner had she gotten that said, when she heard that unmistakable word again.

"Yes?"

It was then that Louise realized that what she had heard was uttered both times immediately after she has said something that included the word "love".

Later that day, when

she was alone, she said the word "love" again. Once again, the same thing happened.

For the next six years, Louise was faced with the situation of being unable to say the word "love" without hearing the voice of Herbie. Always, it was the same.

"Yes?"

It was as if he so desperately wanted to hear that word from her lips that he responded even after death to it. He had had such a bad case of it that the word apparently became the trigger for his response, regardless of how it was used.

The legend of Herbie Tinnerman and Louise Harding doesn't reveal to us the effect of all this on Louise. We don't know if she viewed this situation with Herbie's voice to be a problem or simply as a harmless novelty. The story does tell us, however, that immediately upon her marriage in 1911, the voice no longer came to her when she used the word "love". Perhaps Herbie resigned himself then to the fact that she would never be his.

Nor is it known whether or not the marriage of Louise and Marshall Thayer took place in the little church where Herbie went to convince Louise that he was the man for her.

There has been a lot of water that has flowed past

those hills south of Louisiana since 1911. Undoubtedly there have been a lot of one-way love affairs in the community since then. It's doubtful, however, if any of them have resulted in anything like the strange experiences of Louise Harding.

THE SWAMP COUPLE

There is a swampy area along the river not too far from Quincy. At first glance there is nothing that would suggest the swamp is any different than any other such place found at many sites up and down the Old Mississippi. There is one thing unique about this one, however. On very rare occasions, there will be seen a couple strolling among the cattails. This lady and gentleman are all dressed up in fancy clothes. The reports of the sightings of the pair agree as to what the figures look like.

There has been speculation that the ghostly pair are nothing but marsh gas. Anyone who has seen marsh gas knows, however, that it does not assume well defined shapes; no more than smoke does.

The specific

details observed and reported by those who have seen the ghosts preclude the possibility of such a nebuleous thing as swamp gas as the cause. Quite detailed descriptions of the peoples' clothes and appearances have been given.

No one knows for sure how long this pair has been seen in that swamp, or who they are supposed to be. Perhaps they are fugitives from an old show boat or gambling boat. Maybe they are ghosts of a couple who inadvertently drove into the swamp and perished without anyone knowing it.

Whatever the situation, and whoever the pair is, they haven't been seen for many years. Perhaps it's about time for them to show up again.

RALPH'S HOUSE

ife has never been easy for the poor. It tends to boil down to being a series of problems, differing mainly in their severity. When the Cobb family moved from their farm outside Palmyra to St. Louis in the 1880s, their poverty simply changed from rural poverty to urban. Their hopes that the move would, somehow, provide a better life for their new baby, Ralph, proved to be little more than wishful thinking.

The Cobbs apparently sensed that little Ralph wasn't going to make it. Their granddaughter who told me this story understands that they encouraged the child to play with what few toys they could afford, foreseeing that Ralph would die at a young age. Whether they foresaw the child's death or

not, it did come shortly after they moved
to St. Louis. Ralph's body was returned to
Palmyra, and within a couple of years, they

moved back to the farm.

This story, however, deals with the events
that followed the baby's death and while
they were still living in St. Louis.

Among the few toys that Ralph had was a set
of building blocks. They were said to be
particular favorites of the child. He had
delighted in building a variety of things
with those blocks.

Those blocks, along with his other toys
were packed away in a leather-covered
steamer trunk and stuck under a shelf in
the kitchen. The first time the trunk was

was opened again was in
1886, a few months
after Ralph had died.
Mrs. Cobb was surprised
to find the toys were
pitched in the box,

pretty much at random with one exception. Those building blocks were all neatly arranged to form a miniature house, much like one that Ralph used to build. Seeing that particular design of little house brought tears to Mrs. Cobb's eyes. Obviously, one of the other children had done it, but it reminded her so much of how Ralph would play with those toys hour after hour, especially the blocks.

The other children playing in that trunk did not bother Mrs. Cobb. She, in fact, had gotten into that trunk in order to find a doll for one of the girls. She had to dig around under those blocks to get it so ended up dismantling the little toy house, of course.

A month or so later, she had occasion to get into that trunk again. There, again, she found the blocks arranged into the form of a little house. She thought this was a bit strange, because she knew the children weren't in the habit of playing in there. It was simply too inconvenient to do so under that shelf, and the trunk was far too heavy for them to move it out. She mentioned this to her children and asked who had been playing in trunk. All denied even opening it.

Just before the Cobbs were to move, Mrs. Cobb opened that trunk the third time. Once again the blocks were arranged as before. Once again, she dismantled the little house, this time to make room for a few more toys. She was home alone at the time and had the trunk moved out into the middle of the kitchen floor to put the additional things in it so the family could get moved. She had shut the lid and was wrapping some items in paper to add to the trunk. When she reopened it a few minutes later, it was a totally different story.

No longer could she be so casual about what she saw. Those blocks she had knocked down into a random pile just a few minutes earlier were once again arranged into that familiar little house.

After Mr. Cobb came home and she explained to him what had happened, the couple decided that little Ralph was still with them. They carefully wrapped the blocks in paper, tied the bundle with thread so that little fingers could easily open it, and took the package to Palmyra with them. There the couple buried the package beside the grave of their little boy.

That was the last time that anyone in the Cobb family saw those blocks; at least the last time that Ralph's parents or brothers and sisters saw them.

Mr. and Mrs. Cobb hoped that little Ralph

somehow was able to play again with the little wooden blocks to make his little wooden house with the steep roof and funny little porch.

Perhaps, today, those blocks are neatly stacked again, forming that little house under the sod there in Palmyra.

THE GHOST OF THE
RIVER BEND

ot many ghosts are seasonal ones, but the one who haunts the bend in the Mississippi River below Batchtown, Illinois, shows up only in the winter and only when there is ice cover from shore to shore. Even then, it is seen only infrequently.

The Ghost of the River Bend is probably more properly referred to as the Ghosts of the River Bend for there is both a horse and a rider.

The pair, when seen, is simply going from above Golden Eagle, Illinois, to a point down stream of Old Monroe, Missouri, or the other way. They have been seen by a variety of people over an extended period of time. There was even alleged to have been a sighting during the Civil War.

The need for ice cover in that stretch of the river for the horse and rider to make their way across the river is logical. It's kind of tough for a horse to walk on water, at least a mortal one. On the other hand, there have never been tracks in the snow or gouges in the ice to show the horse was there. I guess ghost aren't bound by logic.

There have been several theories about the ghost rider. It's been speculated that the man is somehow associated with the Civil War, perhaps as a soldier. It's been suggested that he is a farmer of long ago or simply a traveler. All those are only guesses, of course. Perhaps someday we'll find out.

THE STATUE

illie and her carpenter husband Johann had lived in their little house near St. Charles, Missouri for forty-three years by the time 1933 rolled around. One would think that there would be little room for confusion or disagreement as to what was there on the place. After forty-three years, most people pretty well know their home.

In 1933, however, Millie and Johann Bergstrom had found an excep-tion.

The Bergstroms were visiting a daughter over in Jerseyville, Illi-nois. Johann was telling their grandson about an incident that had happened in their back yard. In

telling about the situation, Johann referred to a stone statue that had stood in a
small rock garden there in the yard for
many years.   It was long before the
Bergstroms moved into the home that had
been Millie's parents' home.

The passing reference to the statue was un-
important and really quite incidental to
the point that Johann was making. Millie
picked up on it, however, because of an
error on Johann's part. He had mentioned
that the statue's right arm and hand were
pointing at the ground.

"Why, Johann," Millie interrupted, "that
statue's right hand isn't pointing at anything. Her hand is closed almost like a
fist.

"Whadda mean, like a fist? Her pointin'
finger is straight out and down."

What ensued was a discussion of the
appearance of that right hand. Each of the
contestants teasingly telling the other
that they were gettin' old if they didn't
even know what the statue in their back
yard looked like.

Johann   was
busy explain-
ing that he
had mowed a-
round   that
statue   at
least   two
hundred times,
and   that   he
was   sure   that

he knew what he was talking about on that subject.

The whole discussion kind of petered out when the couple's daughter teased them both for arguing over something that didn't make any difference. Johann's parting shot on the matter was:

"When we get home, I'll give you a tour of the home you've lived in these forty-three years so you'll know what's there."

The subject was pretty well forgotten for the balance of the Bergstrom's visit. It wasn't until they were almost home when Millie observed.:

"Well, I'm lookin' forward to that tour. While we're on the tour, I'll show you that statue's closed right hand."

The discussion, reignited, lasted until they pulled into their drive. The Bergstroms were almost like children as they scurried out to the backyard to prove to each other their respective points.

It was with a triumphant giggle that Millie announced:

"See, you silly old goat! There it is, a fist, if I ever saw one."

There was no arguing about it. There it was; a clenched fist. Johann could only grin and scratch his head.

"Well, I sure thought she was pointin' at the ground. I guess that just goes to show that you don't learn any more mowing a yard two hundred times than you do mowing it once."

Since the issue was now finally settled, it was pretty much forgotten. There was unpacking to do and the yard needed mowing again, as Millie couldn't help but to slyingly observe. The couple got unpacked and Johann decided he'd mow that yard the next day before he got started on a carpentry job he had to do.

So he did, at least he started to. It proved to be the last time he started that chore, however. Johann suffered a massive heart attack and died soon after starting that mowing job.

The gathering of the family commenced immediately, of course. Their daughter and her family who the couple had just visited that week came from Jerseyville as well as other children. Millie's sister from Vandalia, Missouri, came as did other relatives from around the country to comfort Millie and to attend Johann's funeral. Little thought was given to the statue

there in the
back yard.
Millie's fav-
orite old
kitchen range
that Johann
had brought
home when
they first
were married
was cranked
up full force,
turning out
all kinds of
goodies for
all the re-
latives.

As is common
under those
circumstances,
there was
laughter mix-
ed with the tears. Some of the folks
hadn't seen each other for some time so
there was the subdued gaiety of a reunion.

With all the talk and memories shared that
week, the inevitable album of photographs
was drafted for the occasion. Millie was
leafing through the album with her sister,
looking for a particular one of the two of
them on horseback from many years earlier.
As she was hastily shuffling through that
album, one caught her eye. It was of some
of the grandchildren gathered around the
rock garden. Millie's attention fell on
the statue's right hand. There was that
finger extended just as Johann had said it
was!

How could that be? Just a couple of days earlier she and Johann had gone out there especially to see that hand. That granite hand was formed into a fist! Yet here the photograph showed it to be open! As Millie stared at that photo, she realized then that the open hand was, indeed, the way she really remembered it to be. She was wrong about the fist. Yet, there was that fact of the other day. How could it be? How could...

"What's the matter, Millie?" asked her sister, leaning forward. "You look like you've seen a ghost."

Millie started to explain, but could hardly put it in words. The hand of a granite statue simply doesn't change. It can't be open one day and closed the next. Yet there was that photo showing the open hand.

She finally did manage to tell her sister of the situation. When Millie finished her story, her sister looked intently at her.

"Millie, do you remember the stories Mom and Daddy used to tell us when we were kids? Do you remember how they would make popcorn and tell us stories before bedtime?"

"Sure, I do, but what does that have to do with this?" asked Millie.

"Millie, don't you remember how Daddy used to tell us that there was an old story of how the statue in the back yard would close her fist the day before someone was to die?"

Suddenly the images of those evenings of so many years ago came flooding back to Millie. She did, indeed, remember those stories and the popcorn. She did recall her father's stories, including the one about the statue. Until her sister had reminded her, it had laid forgotten in the back of her mind all those years. She realized then that the day they had gotten back from their daughter's in Jerseyville was the day before her husband died.

Almost at the same moment, Millie and her sister ran to look out of the window at the statue there in the back yard. There she was, pointing at the ground, just as in the photo.

The statue is gone now. After Millie died, the place was torn down. Corn now grows where that stone indicator of coming death once stood. Was the statue a ghost? Was there a ghost within it? If so, whose? And why did it foretell of a coming death?

THE NEIGHBOR IN
THE ATTIC

he Briggs family lived in Clarksville, Missouri, overlooking the Mississippi River for many years. They had grown quite accoustomed to the ghostly noise coming from the attic on occasion. It was a chilling sound and was always the same. It started out a low hollow sound. It was almost as if one could feel it rather than hear it. It would seem to go right through a person. The sound would grow in volume until it ended with a "clank." That "ooooo00000MMMMM-clank" sound sent the kids' heads ducking under the covers at night for many years. Even Mrs. Briggs would reach over in the bed to be sure her husband, Roland, was there on those occasions when that eerie sound came filtering down from the attic if it were to happen after she had gone to bed.

For a while the Briggs Family considered moving away but couldn't for one reason or another for a while. Then, when they could, they had grown sufficiently accustomed to their ghost that they didn't bother to leave. Then, too, it became

something of a distinction in the neighborhood to live in a haunted house rather than
the ordinary ones the neighbors had.

So the ghost there in their home and the
Briggs family lived together. The ghost
didn't bother the family very much, and
they didn't bother their supernatural
friend at all. There was talk within the
family, on occasion, about going up and
investigating, but that's all it amounted
to for a long time. The attic was unfin-
ished and didn't even have floor boards.
Were one to walk around up there he would
have to balance himself on the floor joists
or fall through the lath and plaster into
the bedrooms below on the second floor.
Roland Briggs laid the law down rather
firmly. He wouldn't let the children go up
there for fear of their doing just that.
Roland, himself, had no interest in going

up there, and Mrs. Briggs was far too afraid of mice to risk it, so a rather sta-

ble relationship was struck between the ghost in the attic and the occupants of the first two floors.

Every now and then that low mournful sound ending in "clank" would come on down through the house, but nothing would be done to locate its source. As time went by, however, the boys in the family became braver. The "forbidden fruit" theory was at work here, of course. One day the oldest boy just couldn't stand it any more.

"Father, I really think we should go up in the attic to see what's going on with our ghost."

"Nope," his father replied.

"But just think. We might find a chest full of valuable things up there."

"No, sir!, you children don't need to be traspin' around up there stirring up a lot of dust and pokin' yere big feet through the ceiling plaster. Just stay out of there! And just forget it."

So "forget it" they did. The trap door was nailed shut and painted over so the children knew they couldn't sneak up into that attic without the fact being discovered. The children had learned long before that it wasn't advisable to cross their father.

That is, they "forgot it" until the second boy, Jason, went away to college. He was in some class in which there was mention made of the supernatural. Jason couldn't help but brag a little bit about the ghost his family had in their house back in Clarksville. The professor fancied himself to be something of an investigator of the supernatural so took quite an interest in Jason's story. All Jason could tell about, however, was that ooooo00000MMMMM-clank sound since they had never been allowed up in the attic where the sound was coming from. Well, one thing led to another, and Jason's professor ended up coming home with Jason one weekend to look into the situation.

Now, a college professor wanting to investigate the sound was a totally different ballgame than the kids simply wanting to mess around up there so Roland agreed to let the professor go up into the attic to investigate the whole thing. After all, it wasn't every day that the Briggs house had a real live college professor in it. That was almost more exciting than the ghost.

The safari to the attic included the professor, Jason, Roland, and another of the boys. The nails were pulled out of the trap door and that large door was pushed up into the attic. A ladder was positioned and the four fellows proceeded on up. They started up that ladder in an order inversely related to their level of fear. Roland Briggs went first, followed eagerly, if somewhat hesitantly, by the professor. The two boys, however, were suddenly reluctant to even climb the ladder. After all those years of pestering their father, all at once they had second thoughts.

"Maybe, Dad," Jason whispered up from the base of the ladder, "Maybe we ought not to mess around up there. Like you say, we could fall through the ceiling and really mess up the place."

"C'on boys. You been a pesterin' me most your lives to do this. Now let's get on with it since we got started at it.

Meanwhile Mrs. Briggs was standing at the foot of the ladder, knowing full well who would have to clean up the dirt and dust the four men were kicking down onto the carpet below. She knew who would have to wash those filthy clothes when they were done with their messin' around.

By now the four fellows were up there, shining their flashlights around in anticipation of finding their ghost, or at least a chestful of valuable antiques. All they found was an awfully lot of dirt and an old

chicken feeder. For lack of anything
better to do the four men inspected that
old feeder. Besides that, Roland got to
thinking that he could well use that feeder
in the chicken coop out on the farm.

It was while they were studying that feeder
that the professor started to chuckle.

"I think, Jason, that we've found your
ghost," the professor said.

"Why, what do you mean?"

"I think your ghost is actually this old chicken feeder."

The professor went on to explain how the oooooo00000MMMMM-clank sound was probably in that feeder. He pointed out that the drum-like body of the feeder could resonate from air blowing in from a nearby roof vent. He explained how a little cast iron door on the base of the feeder could blow open, then clank shut again.

"I'll bet you," the professor went on, "that the little door would stick shut until a vibration or a mouse would unstick it, thereby allowing the whole process to start again.

"What's that about a mouse?"

The men looked at each other for a moment. Where did that question come from?

"What's that about a mouse?" Mrs. Briggs hollered up again from where she stood at the ladder down below.

"Nothing, Mother," replied Roland.

The professor's explanation was so persuasive and the real source of that strange noise was now so obvious that Jason was embarrassed to have brought it all up. Roland quickly took the opportunity to remind everybody that he never had believed in the ghost idea anyway. Even the professor was not totally free of embarrassment. After all, he had traveled over 200 miles to investigate what turned out to be a rusty old chicken feeder.

To make the best of a bad situation, Mr. Briggs enlisted the aid of the other fellows to help him carry that feeder down to load into the truck so he could have it out on the farm. Jason and the professor left, and Mrs. Briggs cleaned up the mess the men had made.

After all the excitement of the episode and the moving of the feeder out to the farm, things sort of settled back to normal. It was about a month later when the family was all gathered at the table for a holiday dinner. Their ex-ghost was probably about the farthest thing from their minds as they shared all the many things that had happened to each of them.

Then suddenly and almost as if it were more of a feeling than a sound, there came from the attic a loud "oooooOOOOOMMMMM-clank."

"What was that?" asked one of the girls.

"You know very well what that was," replied her father. "That was our old familiar neighbor in the attic."

Jason interrupted, "But my professor explained how that sound came from that old chicken feeder. We brought that down so it isn't even up there any more."

All the eyes of the family then met there
over the dinner table. They all knew then
that the very logical explanation of the
professor's was nice, but that's all it
was. They all knew then that the chicken
feeder had nothing to do with that sound
from the attic.

THE WALKING STICK

illows don't live very long, but they make up for that by living very enthusiastically. Sometimes as they grow so crowded and fast, they seem more like weeds than trees.

A willow twig pushed into the ground will quickly take root and grow into a large tree. More than one surveyor's stake years ago has grown into a tree unique in that it marks the exact location of something or other.

So it was in the early 1870s when a chicken thief was hung from the remains of an old tree down along Wyaconda River west of Canton, Missouri. Now, chicken thieves were not normally hung here in Missouri back in those days. A tar-and feather job was generally considered punishment enough for that crime. There were, however, some feelings in the community that this particular sticky-fingered character had also appropriated a few horses from time to time. Horse theiving was another matter of course. One has to wonder what the

chickens would have thought of that discriminatory policy had they known of it.

With a minimum of judicial niceties and without benefit of such technicalities as a trial, it was decided to make the fellow the honored guest at a necktie party.

I'll not burden the reader with all the details of the event, mainly because I don't know them. One detail that is known, however, deals with the bizarre result of one of the participants stabbing a willow stick in the ground. This fellow had broken off this shaft to use as a "walking stick," a practice we now hardly ever see.

He had poked the stick in the soil as he helped string the hapless chicken thief up. During the process, some of the victim's blood from an arm wound fell onto that stick.

After the grisley affair, the "walking stick" was left there. The owner did not have the stomach to take it. Neither did the two men who came back the following morning to take down the body. The reason being the same as that of the stick's owner; after all, it was only a walking stick and it did have the blood of a dead man on it. So there stood that stick, left after the affair was all over.

Willows being willows, that stick sprouted and took root right where it had been left.

It was known right from the start that the young willow growing there along side that old snag hangin' tree was one that owed its life to the necktie party. It wasn't realized for a few years, however, that there was something even more special about that willow. That special thing was discovered by two boys plinking frogs in the river. It was in the fall and the willow leaves had already started to turn from their summer green to that dirty brown of winter. Some of them down along that river were still green; some were brown and some were in that in-between stage.

Being country boys, these lads sure were surprised to see a willow tree with its leaves the deep rich color of blood. They both noticed it and remarked about how that was such a strange color for a willow tree.

Later that afternoon they told the father of one of them about what they had seen; a red willow tree, of all odd things. The man knew where the boys had been and knew that there were no other kinds of trees down there but willows so couldn't fathom how those kids could have seen that.

The more the man thought about it, the more mystifying it became. He also knew it was in the same area where the hangin' tree had been so the fellow took his son down to the Wyaconda River to have him show him the tree.

If the reader has been paying any attention to this story, he has already figured it out. And that's what it was. That willow tree that had grown from a walkin' stick at the necktie party was showing the color of the blood of that chicken thief that had soiled it years earlier.

Now this lad's father knew his way around trees and knew that willows don't turn red, but this one sure was. This was really somethin'. The next morning he took his neighbor to see this strange thing. By then, however, it was too late. The tree had changed to the same brown as those around it.

The neighbor had exactly twelve months to tease the boy's father about his red willow tree, but only twelve months. The next year when the two men carefully watched it, it did the same thing again. It turned a brilliant rich red color between the green and the brown. It was then that they discovered that the red color lasted only a few hours. Within half a day that odd color was gone and the tree had the typical brown like the others.

A lot of neighbors and a lot of willow trees have come and gone since those days. The original "walkin' stick" tree has long since died, but there has always been one sprout coming from the ground there that is different than any other. It's the one that turns from green to red to brown. The current "sprout" is a tree about ten to twelve inches in diameter. It doesn't exhibit its special display every year anymore. In fact, 1987 was the third year in a row it hasn't. It will probably do it again before long however. the longest it has gone without doing that special thing is four years. For a few brief hours, the Wyaconla River will have its very own unique tree, a red willow. It will be the same red color of the chicken's thief's blood that was hung at that spot back in the early 1870s.

Perhaps this is that man's ghost's way of protesting his having been hung. Maybe he is simply protesting his having been hung over a few lousy chickens.

PERSISTENT STAINS

The soiled area on the wood floor of that large old brick house on a shady street in Hannibal is still there today. Legend has it that the spots are blood from a murder victim back in the days of the Civil War. There are other theories about the origin of those spots, too, but the murder theory is apparently the most prevalent one. The spots are rust colored as blood stains will become with age.

The fact that those stains are still there is not to suggest that the present owner is content to live with them. She isn't. Neither were the previous owners of the house. Numerous attempts have been made to remove the flaws. The floor has been sanded several times, both in that area and in its entirety to get rid of them. Various bleaches and spot removers have been used as well as many many scrubbings with soap and water.

The spots are not difficult to remove. It's keeping them gone that is the problem. They can be cleaned so there is absolutely

no evidence of them remaining at all. Within a few hours, however, they are back just as bright and bold as before.

It's a very fancy and ornate parquet floor with exotic woods so both past the present owners have chosen not to take it up or even to replace the spotted portion. The present owner (and probably previous ones) have been of the impression that there is something supernatural about those spots and have been hesitant to do anything beyond attempting to clean them. The thoroughness with which they can be removed yet come back with such vigor is far different than most stains.

About two years ago, the current resident grew tired of those spots. She had long

since gotten over her initial fear of them.
She just plain grew weary of looking at
them. She had had to look at those ugly
things since she had been a young woman
many years ago.
She came up with
the final solu-
tion and carpet-
ed the room.

The carpetlayers
were a bit per-
plexed by her
insistence that
they place two
layers of foil
over those spots
before laying
the carpet down.
They did it
though, and she
is sure of it
because she
watched to be
sure that they
did.

This lady's
"final solution"
wasn't very fin-
al. Within a
few days her
brand new carpet
was stained in
the same place
and in the same pattern as the spots below.
She has no explanation for that; nor do I.

Today a sofa stands on the floor over the
stain. It isn't the handiest place in the

room for a sofa, but she likes it a whole
lot better than those old stains that go
back many years ago, probably to a murder.
In some way, it appears that the victim of
that murder insists in there being evidence of his or her death there on that
beautiful parquet floor.

OUR VERY OWN COWBOY

real live cowboy along the river is the last thing I expected to find in my research for this book. At least, I guess I found the ghost of one.

This report comes from a lady whose father was a farmer between Florissant and St. Louis. Her account of this story comes from some rather yellowed sheets of stationery her mother, Mrs. Wellman, had used to record the strange events that happened on their farm in the fall of 1922.

It seems that the lane to the Wellman house was a loop that swung off the nearby county road. This loop came by the house and then led back to the county gravel. Its length didn't exceed 200 yards.

During the evening of a late September day in 1922, the family was in the kitchen. They heard the distinct sound of a galloping horse turn off onto the lane. This was not an unusual thing since horses were still used by some of the local farmers at

the time and many rode them for recreation-
al or utilitian purposes. By the time Mr.
Wellman got to the front door, the horse
and rider had traveled the length of their
lane and was once again on the gravel,
still galloping at full tilt.

This episode was soon forgotten. For all
the Wellmans knew, it was simply one of the
neighbor boys who found it to be more fun
to take that loop than it was to stay on
the gravel.

Several more times this happened. When it
began to become a frequent event and late
at night, it became irritating to the
Mellmans.

One night Mr. Wellman happened to be near
the door when they heard those galloping
hooves. He rushed out to lay down the law
to the intruder so as to put a stop to such

foolishness. Late as it was he could still see that the rider and his rig weren't of appearances common to the area. The saddle and the rigging, as well as the man's clothes, were all of a style common to much farther west.

Be the man a farmboy or a cowboy, which-ever, he didn't stop. He rushed past Mr. Wellman, almost knocking him down.

Things were getting serious now. Not only was the man trespassing, but he wasn't pay-ing any attention to obvious at-tempts by Mr. Wellman to stop him. Wellman be-came more than a little mad about the whole affair. For several nights he waited by the door. He was go-ing to put a stop to the whole thing once and for all.

Four nights pass-ed, and Wellman had resolved to stand his post but one or two more before giving it up. He was standing there in the shadow of the porch wondering if it was all worth it. Suddenly he heard those hoofbeats coming. Sure enough, in the light of the moon, he could see the horse-man turn off onto his lane and come gallop-ing toward the house.

Mr. Wellman had planned to only yell to the man to stop him. His anger got the best of him, though. He grabbed the nearest thing he could and took swing at the rider. This turned out to be a stout garden rake leaning on the porch railing. The teeth of that rake caught on the rigging and it was jerked out of his hands. He connected well enough, however, to tear something loose. That fact was momentarily lost to Mr. Wellman for the horse and rider went straight up in the air and disappeared. Now an errant rider who disturbed a perfectly law-abiding farmer was one thing, but one who could disappear right up in the air was something else.

A thoroughly shaken Mr. Wellman finally gathered his wits enough to go back into the house to try to tell his wife what had happened. He found he didn't have to. She had heard the hooves soon enough that she had gotten to the window. She saw the whole thing from thier bedroom, including the rider and his horse going airborne. She was able to offer her husband the comfort of knowing that he wasn't going crazy all by himself, anyway.

It wasn't until the next morning that Mr. Wellman had the presence of mind to check the lane. There were those hoofprints leading to the front of the house and then disappeared just where he had seen the pair rise up in the air. And off to the side lay his rake. Entangled in its tines was an old fashioned spur. It was heavily inlaid with silver and of a style that was later to be determined to have been from a period long before 1922 and from either the southwestern part of the U.S. or from Mexico.

Who was the cowboy and why was he here near Saint Louis? If he was real, how did he disappear up in the air? If he wasn't, why was he wearing a very real spur? No one knows.

Unfortunately, the spur is lost. It was kept in the family for quite a few years but Mr. and Mrs. Wellman are gone now. Their daughter who gave me this story believes the spur was inadvertently stuck in a box of junk sold at the family auction in the late 1930s. Somewhere, perhaps still in Iowa, is a western spur that somehow came to the Mississippi River and became entangled in the tines of an angry farmer's garden rake.

THE BANJO PLAYER

t really wasn't a banjo! That was the firm opinion of one of the young men who saw the ghost known locally near the town of Marblehead, Illinois, as "The Banjo Player."

This young man had been off to college and came up with the lyre theory. The local populace wasn't about to go around puttin' on airs by calling that ghost "The Lyre-player." He was a banjo player, pure and simple.

Whatever it was, The Banjo Player played some kind of instrument. He would be seen and heard along the road between Marblehead and Quincy, just 'a pluckin away on that silly lookin' banjo. When anyone approached too close-ly, he would run away.

This, in itself, was a bit of a departure from standard operating procedure among ghosts. Ghosts are more apt to fade to nothing. This one took the more direct route of running. In fact, the idea of The Banjo Player being a ghost didn't occur to people until two fellows attempted to catch the elusive musician while they were on their horses. One had a quarter horse and the other was on a good stout Morgan horse so could cut right along on them. These fellows were shocked to find their quarry easily pulling away from them even while they were under full gallop. It was then that people realized that The Banjo Player was something more than an ordinary human.

Lots of people saw The Banjo Player over a period of years. He was apt to be seen just about anywhere along the stretch of road from Marblehead to Quincy. He appeared to be of medium build and about twenty to twenty-five years old. The ghost never offered to hurt or threaten anyone. In fact, he was more threatened. People kept trying to catch him, but no one ever did. This was true even of young Eunice Holt who "took a shine" to the young man. She tried to catch him in both a literal sense and figurative one. She too failed, however, eventually marrying a more mortal fellow from down around Kinderhook.

Unlike most ghosts along this stretch of the Mississippi, there were no generally held theories as to who The Banjo Player was. The young college lad had a couple of what otherwise would have been convincing ideas. He, however, lost his crediability after coming up with that lyre theory.

PEARL AND NELLIE

t isn't every ghost that has a flesh and blood alter ego, especially a 2200 pound one. Another way of phrasing that is: "It isn't every horse that has a supernatural counterpart."

That was, however, the situation at the Metcalf farm between Pleasant Hill, Illinois, and its neighboring town, Pittsfield. All this happened many years ago.

This strange circumstance started out ordinarily enough. The farmer, Silas Metcalf, had a matched pair of nice mares for workhorses there on the farm. This wasn't particularly unique, of course, for lots of fellows had matched horses for a team. It wasn't unique when one of the mares died. Nothing odd about that. After all, how many times do both of a team die at the same time? The really unique things started happening after the death of that one mare.

Incidently, the source of this story, Silas's grandnephew, didn't know the names of the mares, so I'm going to name them as a matter of convenience. Furthermore, I'm going to name them Pearl and Nellie. Those were the names of our team when I was a kid on the farm. If I have to come up with names, I might as well immortalize good old Pearl and Nellie a bit.

But, on with the story. When Pearl died, Silas was already in the process of semi-retiring, so he had little reason to replace her. What little playing around he had to do with a team was to drag a little firewood, pull a light wagon, and other such odd chores. This business of using only one horse required some adjustments in the rigging, but Silas preferred that to the bother of getting a replacement for Pearl. Besides that, if he needed to do any heavy work, he could get the team belonging to the neighbor who was farming Silas' place at the time.

Little did Silas realize the strange twist things would take as a result of Pearl's death. He had no way of knowing that Pearl and Nellie would take turns being "the horse" much like identical twins will do to harrass neighbors or their teacher.

The first time Silas realized that something strange was afoot (or ahoof) was the day he hitched Nellie up to a chain to drag some brush he had cut up out of a ditch. He had just finished harnessing that mare when she evaporated into thin air. The harness fell to the ground in a heap and Nellie was gone, just plain gone. Don't think that wasn't a little disconcerting. It's not every-day a horse will up and evaporate on a man.

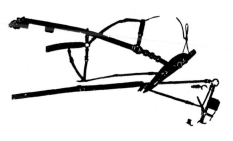

We can only speculate as to Silas's reaction to that situation. Another, and later, episode was even stranger. Silas had been working who he thought was Nellie for several hours. She had all the earmarks of being a mortal horse. She breathed hard after heavy work. She sweat and was bothered by flies. As a good horseman is apt to do, Silas picked up a front hoof to check it for stones or sticks up under the hoof. No sooner had he done that when the leg fell off. Silas didn't have much time to wonder at that for a few seconds later a second leg fell off, then another, and finally the last. There "stood" his mare in mid-air with no visible means of support. Then, suddenly the rest of her body just disappeared as did the four legs lying there on the ground.

Silas was left to carry the heavy harness home alone. The story goes that Silas was more mad than surprised. Apparently, by this time, Silas knew what was going on and was half way accustomed to it.

There were supposedly other incidents like these, and incidents in which Silas mistook his real mare for the ghost one. The other incidents weren't recalled by Silas's grandnephew with the clarity of these two, however.

The reader has to be aware of the fact that Silas lived alone for perhaps too long. A fellow can get to imagining things and seeing things that aren't there if he works alone for too long. After all, ya' gotta' go to town once in a while. Maybe this was the case with Silas Metcalf.

On the other hand, Silas was well known for being totally honest in all his dealings be they business or otherwise. Other folks in the neighborhood were not of the impression that he was off center in any way.

Be all that as it may, the reader will have
to draw his own conclusion as to what went
on, or didn't go on, there at the Metcalf
farm between Pleasant Hill, and Pittsfield
with that pair of mares, one mortal and the
other, not.

THE EXTRA SHADOW

Tim Simpson had heard there was a ghost at that large old white house west of Pittsfield, Illinois, that he bought in the early 1940's. He didn't really care much one way or the other. He didn't even believe in ghosts so had no anticipation that the one said to be in his house would affect him in any way.

Well, maybe that ghost didn't affect him in any important way, but he sure learned to believe in them.

It was one of those cold, but sunny, winter mornings when Tim changed his mind about ghosts. There had been a stiff wind through the night, and some snow already on the ground had drifted rather badly. He could see from the kitchen window that a large drift had completely enveloped the front end of the dog house. He could just

imagine the worried look on his mutt's face as the poor dog was faced with the dilemma of a door completely covered with snow.

Tim slipped on his boots and coat to go out to clear that doorway for the dog. He took along a quart jar of hot water to provide a little heat in the doghouse.

Tim noticed that he was apparently the first one up and out there in the neighborhood. There were no sounds or other evidence there on the shole block of anyone having been out yet that cold morning.

When Tim got to the doghouse to clear that doorway, he chuckled as he heard that tail thumping against the inside wall. He knew the dog was anxious to get out of his wind-blown prison. As he cleared away the door, his four-footed friend gave him a wag of gratitude and proceeded to devour the dog-food Tim had taken along.

Tim had just started back to the house when he saw something he just plain couldn't understand. He saw the tracks he made in the snow as he had trudged out to the dog-house. That, of course, didn't surprise him. What did come as a real shock was that second set that was there in the snow along side of his. He looked up and down the block as he tried to gather his wits sufficiently to figure out what could possibly be going on. No matter how many times he blinked his eyes and looked again, tnere they were.

There were a per-
fectly clear set
of footprints, yet
he knew he was a-
lone. As he stud-
ied them he noti-
ced an interesting
thing. They were
free of any snow
kicked into them.
His own, on the
other hand, had
some snow that had
obviously been
kicked in after he
had made the im-
pression. He de-
duced that whoever
made that second
set had walked be-

hind him to make that happen. All that, of
course, didn't explain who made them or
how. They were really there but not their
maker.

Tim studied the situation for several minutes, not even noticing the bitter cold of
the morning as he tried to figure it all
out. All he could deduce was that they
were made by someone wearing boots and
walking behind him.

Tim stood there a few feet off the path he
had made on the way out to the doghouse.
He was not a particularly imaginative man,
or one given to flights of fancy, but his
normal logic was of no help to him as he
stood there baffled by the situation.

Almost reluctantly, Tim managed to get mov-

ing again back to the house. He steeled himself against the temptation to look behind him as he trudged back toward the door. As he mounted the step or two to the storm door, he stopped with his hand on the latch. He almost dreaded to turn around to see his tracks back to the porch. He was afraid he would see something his practical mind was not prepared to accept. He was afraid he would see two sets of tracks there in the snow again. He had deliberately walked back a few feet away from his trip out in order to make his path obvious. He knew he had no choice but to look.

Finally, as if his eyes had a mind of their own, he found himself forced to look behind him. There was what he had dreaded he would see; a set of tracks beside his own.

Tim's young brother, Paul, lived with him there near Pittsfield. Tim went on into the house and brought Paul to the back door.

"Paul, what do you see there in the snow?"

"Your tracks out to the doghouse and back, why?"

"Do you notice anything odd about them?" asked Tim.

"No, nothing other than you went out there and back twice. Why did you do that? And why do you ask?"

"No reason," Tim replied.

"But why'd you go out there twice in this terrible cold, Tim?" Did you forget the dog-food and have to come back?"

"Yeah, Paul, that's what happened. It's nothing, really."

So who was it that followed Tim out to the doghouse that day, and why? How could he have disappear-ed as Tim stood by the doghouse pondering the situation?

We just don't know.

GHOSTS OF INTERSTATE 90 Chicago to Boston   by D. Latham

GHOSTS of the Whitewater Valley by Chuck Grimes

GHOSTS of Interstate 74   by B. Carlson

GHOSTS of the Ohio Lakeshore Counties   by Karen Waltemire

GHOSTS of Interstate 65   by Joanna Foreman

GHOSTS of Interstate 25 by Bruce Carlson

GHOSTS of the Smoky Mountains by Larry Hillhouse

GHOSTS of the Illinois Canal System by David Youngquist

GHOSTS of the Niagara River   by Bruce Carlson

Ghosts of Little Bavaria   by Kishe Wallace

Shown above (at 85% of actual size) are the spines of other Quixote Press books of ghost stories.
These are available at the retailer from whom this book was procured, or from our office at 1-800-571-
2665 cost is $9.95 + $3.50 S/H.

167

GHOSTS of Lookout Mountain by Larry Hillhouse

GHOSTS of Interstate 77 by Bruce Carlson

GHOSTS of Interstate 94 by B. Carlson

GHOSTS of MICHIGAN'S U. P. by Chris Shanley-Dillman

GHOSTS of the FOX RIVER VALLEY by D. Latham

GHOSTS ALONG I-35 by B. Carlson

Ghostly Tales of Lake Huron by Roger H. Meyer

Ghost Stories by Kids, for Kids by some really great fifth graders

Ghosts of Door County Wisconsin by Geri Rider

Ghosts of the Ozarks B Carlson

Ghosts of US - 63 by Bruce Carlson

Ghosts of Lake Erie by Jo Lela Pope Kimber

GHOSTS OF DALLAS COUNTY   by Lori Pielak

Ghosts of US - 66   by Michael McCarty & Connie Corcoran Wilson

Ghosts of the Appalachian Trail   by Dr. Tirstan Perry

Ghosts of I-70   by B. Carlson

Ghosts of the Thousand Islands   by Larry Hillhouse

Ghosts of US - 23 in Michigan   by B. Carlson

Ghosts of Lake Superior   by Enid Cleaves

GHOSTS OF THE IOWA GREAT LAKES   by Bruce Carlson

Ghosts of the Amana Colonies   by Lori Erickson

Ghosts of Lee County, Iowa   by Bruce Carlson

The Best of the Mississippi River Ghosts   by Bruce Carlson

Ghosts of Polk County Iowa	by Tom Welch
Ghosts of Interstate 75	by Bruce Carlson
Ghosts of Lake Michigan	by Ophelia Julien
Ghosts of I-10	by C. J. Mouser
GHOSTS OF INTERSTATE 55	by Bruce Carlson
Ghosts of US – 13, Wisconsin Dells to Superior	by Bruce Carlson
Ghosts of I-80	by David Youngquist
Ghosts of Interstate 95	by Bruce Carlson
Ghosts of US 550	by Richard DeVore
Ghosts of Erie Canal	by Tony Gerst
Ghosts of the Ohio River	by Bruce Carlson
Ghosts of Warren County	by Various Writers